# THE EASTER LADY

written by Lucille Wood
designed and illustrated by Paul Taylor

# RHYTHMS TO READING
## Book and Record Sets
## A Multi-Sensory Approach to Music and Reading

**A companion recording is available for this book and all others in the RHYTHMS TO READING series. Each picture in this book represents an action song or a descriptive musical composition which is included on the long-playing record.**

The simple text under each picture provides a unique, multi-sensory experience for the young child. He reads about the activities to which he has just responded in movement and song. This text is also included on the recording for classroom use or at the listening post.

On the left-hand page, beginning on page 4, are printed the full story and song lyrics heard on the recording. This page is for the use of teachers, parents and children who have had reading experience.

*Repetition is essential to learning. Learning which might otherwise be derived from tedious drill is here developed in an enjoyable, esthetic context.*

*Research indicates that children learn to read more quickly and easily words that are related to large muscle activity, esthetic experience and tongue-tickling rhymes.*

*When reading experiences are introduced through music, song and vigorous movement*

- *memory is reinforced and tensions released, creating an atmosphere that encourages learning.*

- *the flow of language comes more naturally, encouraging the child to read in complete sentences.*

- *the number of clues which aid the child in reading are multiplied.*

- *word meanings are clarified and sight vocabulary is developed automatically.*

First Printing ......................... January 1971
Second Printing ......................... March 1972

Do you know the Easter Lady?

Do you know the Easter Lady?
Every year at Easter time some boys and girls
and their teacher go out to find the Easter Lady.
They stop at many houses before they find her.
Then what do you think happens?
Let's all go look for the Easter Lady and find out.

Where does the Easter Lady live?

We walk to the first house
with the purple petunias in the front yard.

We knock on the door.
"Good morning. Are you the Easter Lady?"
"No, not I."
"Thank you, anyway, and Happy Easter!"
We go up a little hill and down a little hill
to the second house with the blue shutters.
Skippity, skippity skip.

We knock on the door.
"Good morning. Are you the Easter Lady?"
"No, not I."
"Thank you, anyway, and Happy Easter!"
We go in and out around the trees
to the next house with the pink hollyhocks.
Run, run, run, run, run.

We go from one house to another looking for the Easter Lady.

We knock on the door.
"Good morning. Are you the Easter Lady?"
"No, not I."
"Thank you, anyway, and Happy Easter!"
We go down the walk and around the corner
to the little white house with a yellow door.
Tiptoe, tiptoe.

We knock on the door.
"Good morning. Are you the Easter Lady?"
"Yes, I am the Easter Lady.
Please, sit down on the grass.
I have baked some Easter cookies for you.
You have walked a long way.
While you rest I will tell you an Easter story.
You may help me tell the story
by making pictures with your hands and arms.'

We find the Easter Lady in the house with the yellow door.

"Once upon a time there was a little brown bulb.
It was wrinkled and crinkled and dry
and very unhappy because it was so ugly.
It was crowded into a big basket
with many other bulbs waiting to be sold.
One day Johnny and his mother came into the store
and bought the ugly bulb.
They took it home and put it in a flower pot
and covered it with garden soil.
The poor little bulb hid its head
because it was so frightened and lonely
down in the dark, cold soil.

We listen to a story about a sad little bulb.

"The next day Johnny put the flower pot
outdoors in the sunshine.
The bright round sun warmed the soil
and made the bulb feel a little more comfortable
and cozy. That afternoon a soft breeze sang
a lullaby to the little bulb.
A white, fluffy cloud floated by and a raindrop fell.
Two raindrops, three, four,
and then a shower of raindrops!

The sun and rain made the bulb grow.

"The little bulb was no longer afraid.
It began to reach up through the earth because
it wanted to see the round sun,
the fluffy cloud and the shining raindrops.
It pushed and pushed and pushed
against the earth around it.
In a few days it could feel the warmth of the sun
and leafy arms reached and reached and reached,
higher and higher and higher.

The leaves grew up, up and up.

"The leafy plant heard Johnny talking about Easter.
It wondered what Easter meant.

"One morning when the sun was especially bright,
the little plant lifted its face to the warm sun,
the gentle breeze and the fluffy white clouds.
Johnny and his mother said it was
the most beautiful flower they had ever seen.
The ugly bulb had changed
to a shining white Easter Lily.
The little bulb knew the joy of Easter time."

The sad little bulb became an Easter lily.

"Now we will hide our Easter eggs in the grass.
We will be the Easter rabbits.
Hide each egg in a different place.
The music will help us.
Hippity-hop, hippity-hop."

We hide Easter eggs in the grass, blue, red and yellow.

"The eggs are hidden and we will hunt them.
Hurry, hurry, hurry.
Run, run, run, run, run."

"How many eggs did you find?"

We find the Easter eggs, one, two, three, four, five.

"Easter is a time of little lambs, bunnies,
chicks, ducklings and baby birds.

While we are sitting on the grass,
we will say a little verse about the Easter bunny.
Our hands and fingers will be the little bunny.

*Here are Easter bunny's ears,*
*Here is his little pink nose,*
*This is the way he hippity-hops,*
*Everywhere he goes.*
*This is the way the Easter bunny*
*Climbs up under your chin,*
*Shuts his eyes and goes to sleep,*
*With his little feet tucked in."*

Easter is a time for new things.

"Let's all be little Easter ducklings
while we sing this song.

*I'm an Easter duckling, see me walk along:*
*Wibblety, wobblety, walk, walk,*
*Wibblety, wobblety, walk, walk.*

*I'm an Easter duckling, hear my little song:*
*Quackity, quackity, quack, quack,*
*Quackity, quackity, quack, quack.*

*I'm an Easter duckling, soon I'll learn to fly:*
*Flippity, flappity, flap, flap,*
*Flippity, flappity, flap, flap.*"

We walk like Easter ducklings, wobble, wobble.

"Five children may be the Easter bunnies
in this counting song.

One, two, three, four, five.

*(1) Hippity-hop and hippity-hay, five little bunnies out to play,*
*Hippity-hop and hippity-hay, one little bunny runs away.*

*(2) Hippity-hop and hippity-hay, four little, etc.*

*(3) Hippity-hop and hippity-hay, three little, etc.*

*(4) Hippity-hop and hippity-hay, two little, etc.*

*(5) Hippity-hop and hippity-hay, one little, etc.*

*(6) Hippity-hop and hippity-ho, where did all the bunnies go?*
*Hippity-hop and hippity-ho, only the bunny rabbits know."*

We hop like Easter bunnies. Hippity-hop!

It is time to say good-by and go back to school. "Thank you, Easter Lady, for the happy Easter party. We will see you again next year. Good-by."

We say good-bye to the Easter Lady.

We leave the Easter Lady's house
with the yellow door and run past the house
with the pink hollyhocks.

We skip down a little hill and up a little hill
past the house with the blue shutters.

We walk past the house with the purple petunias
in the front yard.

We hope that all boys and girls
can find an Easter Lady.

We hope that all boys and girls find an Easter Lady.

THE END